Big Bad Bill
and the Baby

Bill was big.

Bill was bad.

"I am big bad Bill," said Bill.

Bill was outside the shop.
"What bad thing can I do?"
said Bill.

Then Bill saw a baby.
The baby's mum was inside
the shop.

LOOK OUT!

Contents

Dee Reid

Story illustrated by
Andrew Painter

Heinemann

In this story

 Big Bad Bill

 The mum

 The baby

Introduce these tricky words and help the reader when they come across them later!

Tricky words

- outside
- what
- inside
- round
- corner
- really
- brick
- saved

Story starter

Big Bad Bill was big and bad. He loved to do bad things. One day, Big Bad Bill went to the shop to find a bad thing to do.

"I see a bad thing I can do," said Bill. "I can hide the baby."

Bill hid the baby round the corner.

"I am really bad," said Bill.

Then a brick fell!

What will the mum think?

7

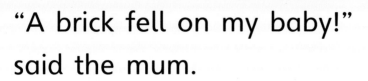

"A brick fell on my baby!"
said the mum.
The mum looked around.
"Where is my baby?"
said the mum.

Then the mum looked round
the corner.
The baby was round the corner.

"You saved my baby!" said the mum. "What a really good thing to do!"

Then the mum gave
Big Bad Bill a **big** kiss.

Quiz

Text Detective

- What bad thing did Big Bad Bill do?
- Why did the mum give Bill a kiss?

Word Detective

- **Phonic Focus**: Blending three phonemes

  Page 6: Can you sound out 'hid'?
- Page 5: Find a word that rhymes with 'ride'.
- Page 8: How many sentences are there on this page?

Super Speller

Read these words:

bad   thing   then

Now try to spell them!

HA! **HA! HA!**

Q What lies in a pram and wobbles?

A A jelly baby!

13

Find out about

- The different materials some buildings are made of

Tricky words

- bricks
- buildings
- guess
- hotel
- glass
- steel
- else
- clue

Introduce these tricky words and help the reader when they come across them later!

Text starter

Lots of buildings are made of bricks but some buildings are not made of bricks. They are made of ice or glass or even something quite surprising!

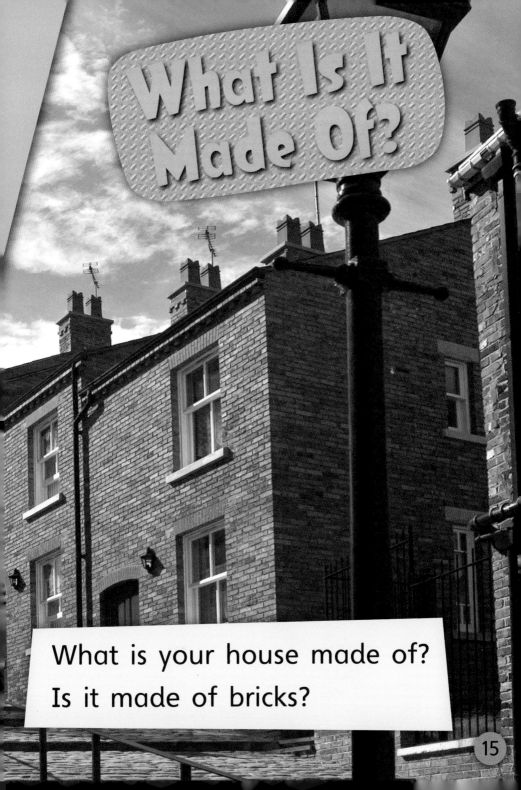

What Is It Made Of?

What is your house made of?
Is it made of bricks?

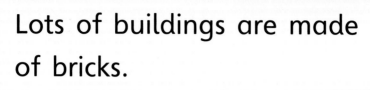

Lots of buildings are made of bricks.

But not all buildings are made of bricks.
Can you guess what this building is made of?

This building is made of ice.
It is an ice hotel.
It has ice walls and ice floors.

Even the tables and chairs are made of ice!

Would you stay in an ice hotel?

Can you guess what this building is made of?

This building is made of glass and steel.

It has glass walls and a glass roof.

So not all buildings are made
of bricks.
Some are made of ice.
Some are made of glass.

Some buildings are made of
something else ...

Can you guess what this
building is made of?
(The cow is a clue!)

Dung buildings
are used to
store cow dung!

Quiz

Text Detective

- What are some buildings made of?
- What new facts have you learned about buildings?

Word Detective

- **Phonic Focus**: Blending three phonemes

  Page 22: Can you sound out 'not'?
- Page 20: Can you find a sentence that is a question?
- Page 18: Can you find the word 'ice' four times on this page?

Super Speller

Read these words:

all you stay

Now try to spell them!

HA! HA! HA!

 Q What did one wall say to the other wall?

A I'll meet you at the corner!